COLLECTIONS FOR YOUNG SCHOLARS™

VOLUME 1 BOOK 2

Keep Trying

Being Afraid

Homes

Art by Colin Bootman

COLLECTIONS FOR YOUNG SCHOLARS™

VOLUME I   BOOK 2

PROGRAM AUTHORS
Marilyn Jager Adams
Carl Bereiter
Jan Hirshberg
Valerie Anderson
S. A. Bernier

CONSULTING AUTHORS
Michael Pressley
Iva Carruthers
Bill Pinkney

OPEN COURT PUBLISHING COMPANY
CHICAGO AND PERU, ILLINOIS

ॐ 4

Printed in the United States of America

ISBN 0-8126-1248-5

15 14 13 12 11

ACKNOWLEDGMENTS

Grateful acknowledgment is given to the following publishers and copyright owners for permission granted to reprint selections from their publications. All possible care has been taken to trace ownership and secure permission for each selection included.

Bayard Presse International: "The Rabbit Warren" by Marie Aubinais, illustrated by Monique Félix from *Pomme d'Api*, No. 236, October 1985, copyright © 1985 by *Pomme d'Api*.

The Child's World, Inc.: An excerpt entitled "Make a Home" from *Animal Habitats: The Best Home of All* by Nancy Pemberton, copyright © 1990 The Child's World, Inc.

Childrens Press, Inc., Chicago: *Animal Homes* by Illa Podendorf, text copyright © 1991 by Childrens Press, Inc.

Clarion Books, an imprint of Houghton Mifflin Co.: *The Little Red Hen* by Paul Galdone, copyright © 1973 by Paul Galdone.

Dutton Children's Books, a division of Penguin Books USA Inc.: *Clyde Monster* by Robert L. Crowe, illustrated by Kay Chorao, text copyright © 1976 by Robert L. Crowe, illustrations copyright © 1976 by Kay Sproat Chorao.

Farrar, Straus & Giroux, Inc.: *The Three Little Pigs*, retold by Margot Zemach, copyright © 1988 by Margot Zemach.

Greenwillow Books, a division of William Morrow & Co., Inc.: *Building a House* by Byron Barton, copyright © 1981 by Byron Barton.

HarperCollins Publishers: "The Kite" from *Days with Frog and Toad* by Arnold Lobel, copyright © 1979 by Arnold Lobel. "The Garden" from *Frog and Toad Together* by Arnold Lobel, copyright © 1971, 1972 by Arnold Lobel. "Goblin Story" from *Little Bear's Visit* by Else Holmelund Minarik, illustrated by Maurice Sendak, text copyright © 1961 by Else Holmelund Minarik, illustrations copyright © 1961 by Maurice Sendak. "Strange Bumps" from *Owl at Home* by Arnold Lobel, copyright © 1975 by Arnold Lobel.

Homeland Publishing, a division of Troubadour Records, Ltd.: *One Light, One Sun*, words and music by Raffi, copyright © 1985 by Homeland Publishing.

Little, Brown and Co. and Walker Books Limited: "The Hare and the Tortoise" and "The Cat and the Mice" from *The Best of Aesop's Fables*, retold by Margaret Clark, illustrated by Charlotte Voake, text copyright © 1990 by Margaret Clark, illustrations copyright © 1990 by Charlotte Voake.

Multimedia Product Development, Inc., Chicago: *My Brother Is Afraid of Just About Everything* by Lois Osborn, text copyright © 1982 by Lois Osborn.

Orchard Books, New York: *Is This a House for Hermit Crab?* by Megan McDonald, illustrated by S. D. Schindler, text copyright © 1990 by Megan McDonald, illustrations copyright © 1990 by S. D. Schindler.

Marian Reiner, for the author: "74th Street" from *The Malibu and Other Poems* by Myra Cohn Livingston (A McElderry Book for Atheneum Publishers), copyright © 1972 by Myra Cohn Livingston.

Scholastic Inc., New York: "Something Is There" from *Spooky Rhymes and Riddles* by Lilian Moore, copyright © 1978 by Lilian Moore.

Martha Shapp: *Let's Find Out About Houses* by Martha and Charles Shapp, illustrated by Tomie dePaola, copyright © 1975 by Franklin Watts, Inc.

Western Publishing Co., Inc.: *Home for a Bunny* by Margaret Wise Brown, illustrated by Garth Williams, copyright © 1956 Western Publishing Co., Inc.

Photography
118 © Nicholas DeVore/Tony Stone Worldwide
   © Robert Frerck/The Stock Market
   © Blair Seitz/Photo Researchers, Inc.
119 © Paul Merideth/Tony Stone Worldwide
   © Focus/Woodfin Camp & Associates
120 © Robert Frerck/Woodfin Camp & Associates
   © Adam Woolfitt/Woodfin Camp & Associates
   © Dan Budnik/Woodfin Camp & Associates
121 © Momatiuk & Eastcott/Woodfin Camp & Associates
   © Traveler's Resource/Tony Stone Worldwide
122 © Porterfield & Chickering/Photo Researchers, Inc.
   © Harry Gruyaert/Magnum
123 © David Hiser/Tony Stone Worldwide
   © Craig Aurness/Woodfin Camp & Associates
124 © David Stoecklein/The Stock Market
   © Hilarie Kavanagh/Tony Stone Worldwide
125 © Claudia Parks/The Stock Market
   © John F. Mason/The Stock Market
126 © Lindsay Hebberd/Woodfin Camp & Associates
   © Michael S. Yamashita/Woodfin Camp & Associates

5

continued on page 191

KEEP TRYING ✻

BEING AFRAID

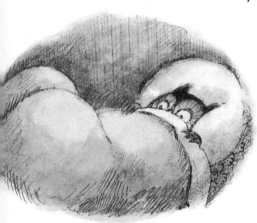

9 ❧

HOMES

KEEP TRYING

THE LITTLE RED HEN

retold and illustrated
by Paul Galdone

Once upon a time a cat and a dog
and a mouse and a little red hen
all lived together in a cozy little house.
The cat liked to sleep all day on the soft couch.

The dog liked to nap all day
on the sunny back porch.

And the mouse liked to snooze all day
in the warm chair by the fireside.

So the little red hen had to do
all the housework.

She cooked the meals and washed
the dishes and made the beds.
She swept the floor and washed
the windows and mended the clothes.
She raked the leaves and mowed the grass
and hoed the garden.

One day when she was hoeing the garden
she found some grains of wheat. "Who will plant
this wheat?" cried the little red hen.

"Not I," said the cat.

"Not I," said the dog.

"Not I," said the mouse.

"Then I will," said the little red hen. And she did.

Each morning the little red hen watered the wheat and pulled the weeds.

Soon the wheat pushed through the ground and began to grow tall.

When the wheat was ripe, the little red hen asked, "Who will cut this wheat?"

"NOT I," said the cat.

"NOT I," said the dog.

"NOT I," said the mouse.

"Then I will," said the little red hen. And she did.

When the wheat was all cut, the little red hen asked, "Now, who will take this wheat to the mill to be ground into flour?"

"Not I," said the cat.

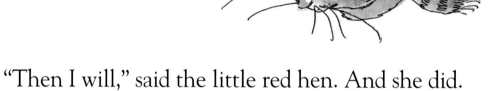

"Not I," said the dog.

"Not I," said the mouse.

"Then I will," said the little red hen. And she did.

The little red hen returned from the mill
carrying a small bag of fine white flour.
"Who will make a cake from this fine
white flour?" asked the little red hen.

"Not I," said the cat.

"Not I," said the dog.

"Not I," said the mouse.

"Then I will," said the little red hen. And she did.

She gathered sticks and made a fire in the stove.
Then she took milk and sugar and eggs
and butter and mixed them in a big bowl
with the fine white flour.

When the oven was hot she poured the cake
batter into a shining pan and put it in the oven.

Soon a delicious smell filled the cozy little house.

The cat got off the soft couch and strolled
into the kitchen.

The dog got up from the sunny back porch
and came into the kitchen.

The mouse jumped
down from his warm
chair and scampered
into the kitchen.

The little red hen
was just taking a
beautiful cake out
of the oven.

"Who will eat this cake?" asked the little red hen.
"I WILL!" cried the cat.
"I WILL!" cried the dog.
"I WILL!" cried the mouse.

But the little red hen said, "All by myself I planted the wheat, I tended the wheat, I cut the wheat, I took the wheat to the mill to be ground into flour. All by myself I gathered the sticks, I built the fire, I mixed the cake. And all by myself I am going to eat it!"

And so she did, to the very last crumb.

After that, whenever
there was work to be done,
the little red hen had
three very eager helpers.

THE KITE

Arnold Lobel

Frog and Toad went out to fly a kite.
They went to a large meadow
where the wind was strong.
"Our kite will fly up and up," said Frog.
"It will fly all the way up
to the top of the sky."
"Toad," said Frog,
"I will hold the ball of string.
You hold the kite and run."

Toad ran across the meadow.
He ran as fast as his short legs
could carry him.
   The kite went up in the air.
   It fell to the ground with a bump.

Toad heard laughter.
Three robins were
sitting in a bush.
   "That kite will not fly,"
said the robins.
"You may as well give up."

Toad ran back to Frog.
"Frog," said Toad,
"this kite will not fly.
I give up."
   "We must make a second try,"
said Frog. "Wave the kite
over your head.
Perhaps that
will make it fly."

Toad ran back
across the meadow.
He waved the kite
over his head.
The kite went up in the air
and then fell down with a thud.

"What a joke!" said the robins.
"That kite will never
get off the ground."

Toad ran back to Frog.
"This kite is a joke," he said.
"It will never get off the ground."
    "We have to make
a third try," said Frog.
"Wave the kite over your head
and jump up and down.
Perhaps that will make it fly."

Toad ran across the meadow again.
He waved the kite over his head.
He jumped up and down.
The kite went up in the air and
crashed down into the grass.

"That kite is junk,"
said the robins.
"Throw it away and go home."

Toad ran back to Frog.
"This kite is junk," he said.
"I think we should
throw it away and go home."
    "Toad," said Frog,
"we need one more try.
Wave the kite over your head.
Jump up and down
and shout UP KITE UP."
    Toad ran across the meadow.
He waved the kite over his head.
He jumped up and down.
He shouted, "UP KITE UP!"
    The kite flew into the air.
It climbed higher and higher.

"We did it!" cried Toad.

"Yes," said Frog.
"If a running try
did not work,
and a running and waving try
did not work,
and a running, waving,
and jumping try
did not work,
I knew that
a running, waving, jumping,
and shouting try
just had to work."

29

The robins flew out of the bush.
But they could not fly
as high as the kite.
Frog and Toad sat and watched their kite.
It seemed to be flying
way up at the top of the sky.

74TH STREET

Myra Cohn Livingston

illustrated by Stella Ormai

Hey, this little kid gets roller skates.
She puts them on.
She stands up and almost
flops over backwards.
She sticks out a foot like
she's going somewhere and
falls down and
smacks her hand. She
grabs hold of a step to get up and
sticks out the other foot and
slides about six inches and
falls and
skins her knee.

      And then, you know what?

She brushes off the dirt and the
blood and puts some
spit on it and then
sticks out the other foot

    again.

31 ⅔

FINE ART
KEEP TRYING

First Steps. 1943. Pablo Picasso.

Oil on canvas. Gift of Stephen C. Clark, B.A., 1903, Yale University Art Gallery.
© 1994 ARS, NY/SPADEM, Paris

Study for the Munich Olympic Games Poster. 1971. Jacob Lawrence.

Gouache on paper. Purchased with funds from PONCHO, Seattle Art Museum. 79.31. Photo: Paul Macapia

33

The Flower Carrier. 1935. Diego Rivera.

Oil and tempera on masonite, 121.9 x 121.3 cm. Albert M. Bender Collection, Gift of Albert M. Bender in memory of Caroline Walter, San Francisco Museum of Modern Art

THE GARDEN

Arnold Lobel

Frog was in his garden.
Toad came walking by.
   "What a fine garden
you have, Frog," he said.
   "Yes," said Frog. "It is very nice,
but it was hard work."
   "I wish I had a garden," said Toad.
   "Here are some flower seeds.
Plant them in the ground," said Frog,
"and soon you will have a garden."
   "How soon?" asked Toad.
   "Quite soon," said Frog.

Toad ran home.
He planted the flower seeds.
"Now seeds," said Toad,
"start growing."

Toad walked up and down
a few times.
The seeds did not start to grow.
Toad put his head
close to the ground
and said loudly,
"Now seeds, start growing!"

Toad looked at the ground again.
The seeds did not start to grow.
Toad put his head
very close to the ground and shouted,
"Now seeds, start growing!"

Frog came running up the path.
"What is all this noise?" he asked.
"My seeds will not grow," said Toad.
"You are shouting too much," said Frog.
"These poor seeds are afraid to grow."

"My seeds are afraid to grow?"
asked Toad.
"Of course," said Frog.
"Leave them alone for a few days.
Let the sun shine on them,
let the rain fall on them.
Soon your seeds will start to grow."

That night Toad looked out of his window.

"Drat!" said Toad.

"My seeds have not started to grow.
They must be afraid of the dark."

Toad went out to his garden with some candles.

"I will read the seeds a story," said Toad.

"Then they will not be afraid."

Toad read a long story to his seeds.

All the next day
Toad sang songs
to his seeds.

And all the next day
Toad read poems
to his seeds.

And all the next day
Toad played music
for his seeds.

Toad looked at the
ground. The seeds still
did not start to grow.

"What shall I do?"
cried Toad. "These must be
the most frightened seeds
in the whole world!"

Then Toad felt very tired, and he fell asleep.

"Toad, Toad, wake up," said Frog.
"Look at your garden!"

Toad looked at his garden.
Little green plants were coming up
out of the ground.

"At last," shouted Toad,
"my seeds have stopped
being afraid to grow!"

"And now you will have
a nice garden too," said Frog.

"Yes," said Toad,
"but you were right, Frog.
It was very hard work."

A SURPRISE FOR MOM

Anita Bosquez

illustrated by Cat Bowman Smith

Andy was planning to bake a surprise cake
for Mom's birthday.

"I want to surprise Mom, too,"
said Sara. "Please? Please? Pretty please?"

A big brother can only take so much.
Andy gave in.

"Okay," he said. "Go find a surprise
to put into the cake."

That would keep her busy.

There was no peanut butter. No jelly.
No ketchup. No grapes.
What could Sara find?

Nuts! Raisins!
Mom loved them.

Oops!
Nuts on the floor. Raisins on the floor.

44

"Here's a surprise for the cake," said Sara.

"So soon?" asked Andy.

"Now what can I do?" said Sara.

Andy thought for a minute.

"You can beat the eggs."

That would keep her busy.

"Watch out, eggs. Here I come!"

47

Sara beat the first two eggs
very, very well. Then she started on the next two.
"Stop!" Andy yelled. "Don't beat them that way!"
Oops!

"I'll beat the eggs,"
Andy said. "You get the flour."
Maybe that would keep her busy.

Look who's home!
"Surprise, Mom!" said Sara.

"Oh, Mom," said Andy.
"I wanted to surprise you with a cake."
"And I helped," said Sara.
"I see you did," said Mom.
"I don't think I can stand many
surprises like this!"

"I knew you'd be surprised,"
said Sara.
"HAPPY BIRTHDAY, MOMMY!"

THE FOX AND THE GRAPES

Aesop

illustrated by Bob Barner

One day a fox was running
down a dusty road.
He was hot and thirsty.
Soon he saw some grapes
hanging on a vine in a garden.
The grapes were large and ripe
and juicy.
They looked very tasty
to the hot, thirsty fox.
"How I wish I had some
of those grapes," said the fox.

52

The fox jumped high in the air.
He reached up with his paw,
but he did not get the grapes.
He jumped higher and higher,
but he still could not get the grapes.
At last the fox gave up.
"Those grapes can stay on the vine,"
said the fox.
"I can tell that they are sour.
They must taste awful.
I don't like sour grapes."

53

THE HARE AND THE TORTOISE

A Shared Reading Story
Aesop
retold by Margaret Clark
illustrated by Charlotte Voake

A hare was one day making fun of a tortoise. "You are a slowpoke," he said. "You couldn't run if you tried."

"Don't laugh at me," said the tortoise. "I bet that I could beat you in a race."

"Couldn't," replied the hare.

"Could," replied the tortoise.

"All right," said the hare. "I'll race you. But I'll win, even with my eyes shut."

They asked a passing fox to set them off.

"Ready, set, go!" said the fox.

The hare went off at a great pace. He got so far ahead he decided he might as well stop for a rest. Soon he fell fast asleep.

The tortoise came plodding along, never stopping for a moment.

When the hare woke up, he ran as fast as he could to the finish line.

But he was too late—the tortoise had already won the race!

BIBLIOGRAPHY

Angelina Ballerina
by Katharine Holabird
Angelina the mouse wants
to become a ballerina.
Does she make it?

Fox on the Job
by James Marshall
Fox has to earn his own money for a
new bike.

If At First . . .
by Sandra Boynton
A mouse must move an
elephant up the hill. How will he do it?

I Never Win!
by Judy Delton
Charlie thinks he'll never win at sports.
He is surprised to find that he can win
when he tries hard.

Katy and the Big Snow
by Virginia Lee Burton
Katy the tractor helps dig a city
out from a very big snow storm.

Little Toot
by Hardie Gramatky
A little tugboat likes to play, not work.
Then he becomes a hero during a storm.

Mike Mulligan and His Steam Shovel
by Virginia Lee Burton
Mary Anne the steam shovel
tries to dig a cellar in just one day.

Whistle for Willie
by Ezra Jack Keats
Peter tries hard to learn to
whistle so he can call to his dog.

BEING AFRAID

59

MY BROTHER IS AFRAID OF JUST ABOUT EVERYTHING

A Shared Reading Story

Lois Osborn

illustrated by Loretta Krupinski

 60

My little brother is afraid
of just about everything.
Whenever there's a thunderstorm,
I know where to find him.
Underneath the bed.

When we're outside and the mailman comes, I know where to find him. Behind the bushes.

He doesn't like men with beards.

When he's in the bathtub, he screams if I let the water out. Maybe he thinks he'll go down the drain along with the water.

So I take him out first. Then I empty the tub.

Yesterday my mother
started to vacuum.
My brother started to howl.
Maybe he thinks
the vacuum cleaner is a monster.
He sure acts that way. So my mother
asked me to take him for a walk.
We went past my school. "See?" I said.
"That's where you'll be going in a couple of years."
I could tell by my brother's face
what he thought about *that*.

We met some of my friends
at the playground.
They think my brother is cute.
"What's your name?" and
"How old are you?" they asked.
    Did my brother answer them?
No-o-o, of course not.
    He just buried his face in my stomach,
the way he always does.

On our way home, we came to some railroad
tracks. A train was coming, so we waited to cross.

Most kids think trains are pretty exciting.
They wave at the engineer. They count cars.
But not my brother.

His arms went around me like boa constrictors.
I couldn't have shaken him loose if I'd wanted to.

Back home, we sat together
under the big tree in our backyard.
I decided it was time
we had a talk.

"Look," I said to him,
"did thunder and lightning
ever hurt you?"
He shook his head.

"Or the mailman,
or the vacuum cleaner?"
He shook his head again.

"Then how come you're so scared
of everything?" I asked.

My brother's face drooped.
The corners of his mouth
turned down and quivered.
His shoulders came up to his ears.
His big eyes looked at me.
    I felt like patting him
on the back and saying
that everything was okay.
    But instead I said,
"Look, you've got to get tough.
It's stupid to keep on being afraid
of things that won't hurt you."

    Then I saw a great big, happy smile
spread across my brother's face.
He was looking at something behind me.
I didn't even have to ask what it was.

65

Nothing else could make my brother look that happy. It had to be—a dog!

I tried. I tried very hard.

I shut my eyes and pretended the dog wasn't there.

I took deep breaths so my heart wouldn't beat so fast.

I clenched my hands so they would stop trembling.

I prayed the dog would go away.

Then I felt its feet upon my shoulders. I thought of sharp claws.

I felt its rough, wet tongue against the back of my neck. I thought of all those teeth.

That did it!

I couldn't get into the house fast enough! Across the yard I ran. I yanked open the screen door and quickly slammed it shut. I even hooked it.

Safe behind the door, I stood, catching my breath.

Then I went to the window. I knew what I would see.

Yes, there was my brother, with his arms around that dog.

I watched them play together. I watched them for a long time.

I suppose that dog would have played with me, too, if I had been outside.

But I stayed inside.

I felt bad about it, but I stayed inside.

Oh well, everybody's afraid of something, I guess.

GOBLIN STORY

Else Holmelund Minarik

illustrated by Maurice Sendak

One day a little goblin went by an old cave.
It was old, it was cold, it was dark.

And something inside it went bump.

What was that?

BUMP!

"Hoo—ooh—" cried the goblin.

He got so scared that he jumped
right out of his shoes.
Then he began to run.

Pit–pat–pit–pat–pit–pat—
What was that?
SOMETHING was running after him.

Oh my goodness, what could it be?
The goblin was too scared to look back.
He ran faster than ever.
But so did the SOMETHING that went
pit–pat–pit–pat–pit–pat—

The goblin saw a hole in a tree.
He jumped inside to hide.
The pit–pat–pit–pat came closer,
closer—CLOSER—till it stopped,
right by the hole in the tree!

73

Then all was quiet.
Nothing happened.
Nothing.

The little goblin wanted to peek out.
It was so quiet.
Should he peek out?

Yes, he would. He WOULD peek out!
And he did.

"Eeeeeh—!" cried the goblin.
Do you know what he saw?

He saw—his SHOES!
His own little shoes—
and nothing more.
"Goodness," said the goblin,
hopping out of the tree.

77

"That old bump in the cave
made me jump right out of my shoes.
But they came running after me,
didn't they!
And here they are!"

He picked up his shoes, hugged them,
and put them back on.
"Good little shoes," said the goblin.
"You didn't want to stay behind,
did you!" He laughed.

"Who cares about an old bump,
anyway," he said.
So he snapped his fingers,
and skipped away—
just like that!

SOMETHING IS THERE

Lilian Moore

illustrated by Toni Goffe

Something is there
there on the stair
coming down
coming down
stepping with care.
Coming down
coming down
slinkety-sly.
Something is coming and wants to get by.

80

STRANGE BUMPS

Arnold Lobel

Owl was in bed. "It is time
to blow out the candle and go to sleep,"
he said with a yawn.
 Then Owl saw two bumps
under the blanket at the bottom of his bed.
"What can those strange bumps be?" asked Owl.

Owl lifted up the blanket.
He looked down into the bed.
All he could see was darkness.
Owl tried to sleep,
but he could not.

"What if those two strange bumps
grow bigger and bigger
while I am asleep?" said Owl.
"That would not be pleasant."

83 ❦

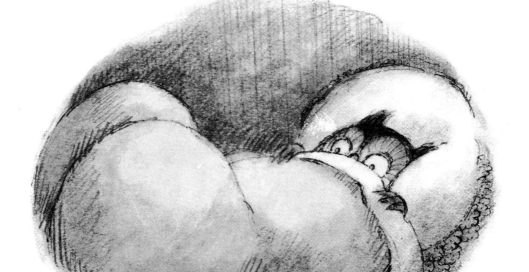

Owl moved his right foot
up and down.
The bump on the right
moved up and down.
"One of those bumps
is moving!" said Owl.
Owl moved his left foot
up and down.
The bump on the left
moved up and down.
"The other bump
is moving!" cried Owl.

Owl pulled
all of the covers
off his bed.
The bumps were gone.
All Owl could see
at the bottom of the bed
were his own two feet.

"But now I am cold," said Owl.
"I will cover myself
with the blankets again."
As soon as he did,
he saw the same two bumps.
"Those bumps are back!" shouted Owl.
"Bumps, bumps, bumps!
I will never sleep tonight!"

Owl jumped up and down
on top of his bed.
"Where are you?
What are you?" he cried.
With a crash and a bang
the bed came falling down.

Owl ran
down the stairs.
He sat in his chair
near the fire.

"I will let those two strange bumps
sit on my bed
all by themselves," said Owl.
"Let them grow
as big as they wish.
I will sleep right here
where I am safe."

And that is what he did.

LITTLE MISS MUFFET
Nursery Rhyme
illustrated by Dominic Catalano

Little Miss Muffet sat on her tuffet,
Eating her curds and whey;
Along came a spider and sat down beside her
And frightened Miss Muffet away.

CLYDE MONSTER

Robert L. Crowe
illustrated by Kay Chorao

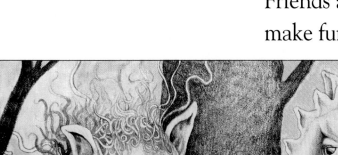

Clyde wasn't very old,
but he was growing—
uglier every day.

He lived in a large forest
with his parents.

Father Monster was a big, big monster
and very ugly, which was good.
Friends and family usually
make fun of a pretty monster.

Mother Monster
was even uglier
and greatly admired.
All in all, they were
a picture family—
as monsters go.

Clyde lived in a cave.
That is, he was supposed to
live in a cave,
at night anyway.
During the day,
he played in the forest,
doing typical monster things
like breathing fire at the lake
to make the steam rise.

He also did typical Clyde things
like turning somersaults
that made large holes in the ground,
and generally bumping into things.
He was more clumsy than the average monster.

At night, Clyde was supposed to
go to his cave and sleep.
That's when the trouble started.
He refused to go to his cave.

"Why?" asked his mother.
"Why won't you go
to your cave?"

"Because," answered Clyde,
"I'm afraid of the dark."

"Afraid," snorted his father
until his nose burned.
"A monster of mine afraid?
What are you afraid of?"

"People," said Clyde.
"I'm afraid there are people
in there who will get me."
"That's silly," said his father.
"Come, I'll show you."
He breathed a huge burst of fire
that lit up the cave.
"There. Did you see any people?"
"No," answered Clyde.
"But they may be hiding
under a rock
and they'll jump out and get me
after I'm asleep."

93

"That is silly," pointed out his mother
with her pointed tongue.
"There are no people here.
Besides, if there were,
they wouldn't hurt you."

"They wouldn't?" asked Clyde.

"No," said his mother.
"Would you ever hide
in the dark under a bed
or in a closet
to scare a human boy or girl?"

"Of course not!" exclaimed Clyde,
upset that his mother
would even think of such a thing.

"Well, people won't hide
and scare you either.
A long time ago
monsters and people made a deal,"
explained his father.
"Monsters don't scare people,
and people don't scare monsters."

"Are you sure?" Clyde asked.

"Absolutely," said his mother.
"Do you know of a monster
who was ever frightened
by a people?"

"No," answered Clyde
after some thought.

"Do you know of any boys or girls
who were ever frightened by a monster?"
"No," he answered quickly.
"There!" said his mother.
"Now off to bed."
"And no more nonsense
about being scared by people,"
ordered his father.

"Okay," said Clyde
as he stumbled into the cave.
"But could you leave the rock open
just a little?"

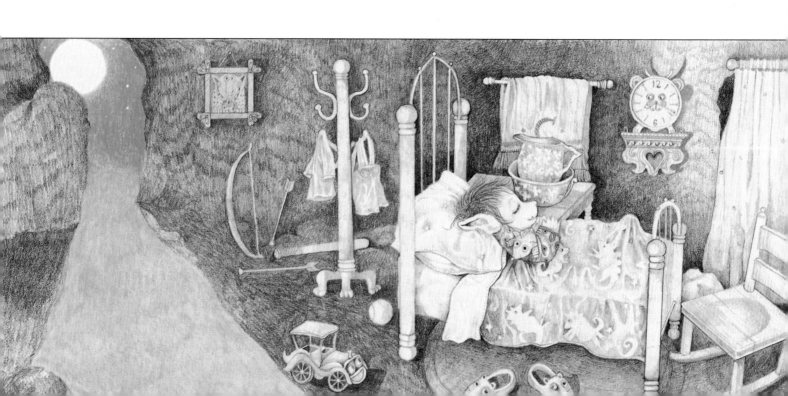

FINE ART
BEING AFRAID

Cat trying to catch a goldfish. c. 1838–1840. Utagawa Kuniyoshi.

Color woodcut. Gift of Mrs. John D. Rockefeller, Philadelphia Museum of Art

The Gulf Stream. 1899. Winslow Homer.

Oil on canvas. Catharine Lorillard Wolfe Collection, Wolfe Fund, 1906, The Metropolitan Museum of Art.
Photo: ©1994 The Metropolitan Museum of Art

His First Lesson. 1903. Frederic Remington.

Oil on canvas. Amon Carter Museum, Fort Worth, Texas. 1961.231

THE CAT AND THE MICE

Aesop
retold by Margaret Clark
illustrated by Charlotte Voake

A family of mice was being chased every day by a hungry cat.

"What are we going to do?" said Mother, as they all sat around her one evening.

Everyone had something to suggest, but the smallest mouse said, "If we hang a bell around his neck, then we shall hear him coming and we'll have time to get out of his way."

All the mice squealed in excitement and told the smallest mouse how clever he was.

Then the oldest mouse in the family spoke. "That may *sound* like a good idea," he said, "but tell me: which one of you is brave enough to go up to the cat and hang a bell around his neck?"

And why do you think none of them answered?

BIBLIOGRAPHY

Bedtime for Frances
by Russell Hoban
Frances has a hard time going to sleep
when she sees and hears things
in her room.

Granny Is a Darling
by Kady MacDonald Denton
Billy scares away the monsters
when Granny comes to visit.

I Hear a Noise
by Diane Goode
This is a silly story where monsters
have mothers, too.

I'll Protect You from the Jungle Beasts
by Martha Alexander
A small boy and his teddy bear
walk through the scary woods.

Sleep Out
by Carol and Donald Carrick
Christopher hears strange sounds
when he sleeps outside for the first time.

Storm in the Night
by Mary Stolz
On a dark and stormy night,
Grandfather tells Thomas
about another storm long ago.

There's a Nightmare in My Closet
by Mercer Mayer
A boy faces his nightmare
in a way that will make you laugh.

Will It Be Okay?
by Crescent Dragonwagon
A mother tells her little girl
what to do when she is afraid.

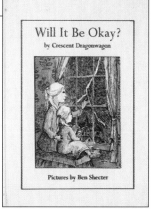

103

HOMES

LET'S FIND OUT ABOUT HOUSES

A Shared Reading Essay
Martha and Charles Shapp
illustrated by Tomie dePaola

Everybody lives in a house.
But not all houses are the same.
There are many different kinds of houses.

Houses are of different sizes.
Some people live in big houses.
Some houses are so big that many families can live
in one house.

Some people live in small houses.

Some people live in tiny houses.

Houses are of different shapes.

The roofs of some houses are pointed.
The roofs of some houses are flat.

Houses are made of different things.

Many houses are made of wood.

Many houses are made of brick.

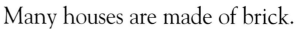

Some houses are made of
things people can get easily.
Eskimos sometimes make
their houses of snow and ice.

People who live
in the rain forest
sometimes make
their houses of grass.

People who live in the woods
often build their houses of logs.

People who live in the
mountains often build
their houses of stones.

Some people live in houses made of mud.
They make bricks out of mud.
They build houses with the bricks.

Houses protect people from
the weather.
Houses keep out the cold.

Houses protect people
from the hot sun.

Houses keep out
the rain.

Houses keep out
the snow.

Houses keep people safe.
Some people who live near
rivers build their houses on stilts.
No matter how high the river
rises, the people are safe.
There are some people who build
houses in trees.
The tree houses protect the people
from wild animals.

There are people who like to move
from place to place.
They live in houses that can be
moved easily.

A trailer house can
be moved easily.

A houseboat can move easily.

Some people live in tents in the desert.
Tents can be carried easily from place to place.

Most people build their houses near one another.
People like neighbors whether they live
on a desert, in a forest, or in a city.

  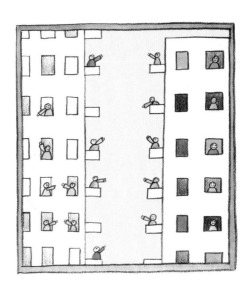

It doesn't matter what
size a house is.
It doesn't matter what
shape a house is.
It doesn't matter what a
house is made of.
Houses keep people safe and
comfortable and happy.

113

BUILDING A HOUSE

Byron Barton

On a green hill a bulldozer
digs a big hole.

Builders hammer and saw.

A cement mixer pours
cement.

Bricklayers lay large white blocks.

Carpenters come and
make a wooden floor.

They put up walls.

They build a roof.

A bricklayer builds a fireplace
and a chimney too.

A plumber puts in pipes for water.

An electrician wires for electric lights.

Carpenters put in windows and doors.

Painters paint inside and out.

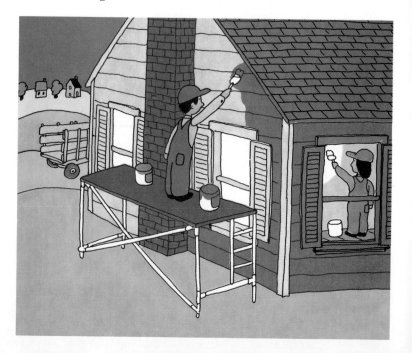

The workers leave.

The house is built.

The family moves in.

ONE LIGHT, ONE SUN

song by Raffi

essay text by Deborah Eaton

This song will show you many homes
and many faces
in many different far-off places.

Lesotho,
South Africa

Argentina

The Philippines

Cliff houses are cool
when the sun is hot.

Jordan

It's not too hot here.
Grass grows on a roof.

Germany

One light, one sun,
one sun lighting everyone.

A reed hut
is made of dried plants.

Peru

Flowers make this home
pretty.

Austria

You need a ladder
to get to some
pueblo houses.

New Mexico, USA

One world turning,

His house has a tin roof.

Poland

Their house is up on stilts.

The Philippines

One world turning everyone.

Some homes float.

Hong Kong

Nevada, USA

Trailers are homes on wheels.

One world, one home,
one world home for everyone.

People can even turn palm leaves into a home.

Guatemala

Morocco

Some homes fold right up.

One dream, one song,
one song heard by everyone.

A fireplace
warms a home.

New Mexico,
USA

A porch is a nice place to sit.

Thailand

One love, one heart,
one heart warming everyone.

Doors are for friends coming in.

Brazil

Windows let light in
and let people smile out.

Argentina

One hope, one joy,
one love filling everyone.

Big and tall . . .

Indonesia

Round and small . . .

Somalia

One light, one sun,
one sun lighting everyone.

and homes are for enjoying.

Utah, USA

All over the world,
homes are for living . . .

Sudan

One light warming everyone.

ONE LIGHT, ONE SUN

128

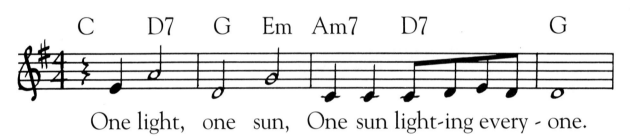

One light, one sun, One sun light-ing every - one.

One world turn - ing, One world turn-ing every - one.

One world, one home,
One world home for everyone.
One dream, one song,
One song heard by everyone.

One love, one heart,
One heart warming everyone.
One hope, one joy,
One love filling everyone.

Part Two of My Village, in Yorubaland, Nigeria, Africa. c. 1980–1990. Chief Z.K. Oloruntoba.

Plant dyes on fabric. Collection of the artist. Photo: Suzanne Kaufman

Miniature funerary model of a house. Han dynasty, (202 B.C.–A.D. 220). Chinese.

Pottery. Musée Cernuschi, Paris. Photo: Giraudon/Art Resource

 130

Making Tent for Winter. 1974. Malaya Akulukjuk.

Stencil print by Solomon Karpik, Pangnirtung Print Shop, 1975. Canadian Museum of Civilization

FINE ART
HOMES

Three Figures on Red and Blue Houseboat.
c. 1939–1947. Bill Traylor.

Poster paint and pencil on cardboard. Collection of Judy Saslow.
Photo: Carl Hammer Gallery, Chicago

Street Scene—Gloucester. c. 1940. Edward Hopper.

Oil on canvas. Edwin and Virginia Irwin Memorial Collection, Cincinnati Art Museum

THE THREE LITTLE PIGS

retold and illustrated
by Margot Zemach

Long ago, three little pigs
lived happily with their momma pig.
But the day came when their momma
told them it was time for them
to go out into the world.

"Build good, strong houses,"
she said, "and always watch out
for the wolf. Now goodbye,
my sons, goodbye."

As the first little pig
was going along,
he met a man
who was gathering straw.

"Please, sir," he said,
"give me some straw
to build me a house."

So the man gave him some straw
and the first little pig
built himself a house.

One day the wolf
came knocking at his door.
"Little pig, little pig,"
he called. "Let me come in!"
But the first little pig said:
"No, no, I won't let you in—
not by the hair of my chinny-chin-chin."
"Well then," said the wolf,
"I'll huff and I'll puff
and I'll blow your house down."
So he huffed and he puffed
and he blew the house down,
and he ate up the first little pig.
Yumm-yum!

As the second little pig
was going along,
he met a man
with a load of sticks.

"Please, sir," he said,
"give me some sticks
to build me a house."

So the man gave him some sticks
and the second little pig
built himself a house.

135 🐘

One day the wolf
came knocking at his door.
"Little pig, little pig,"
he called. "Let me come in!"
But the second little pig said:
"No, no, I won't let you in—
not by the hair of my chinny-chin-chin."
"Well then," said the wolf,
"I'll huff and I'll puff
and I'll blow your house down."
So he huffed and he puffed
and he huffed and he puffed
and he blew the house down,
and he ate up the second little pig.
Yumm-yum!

As the third little pig
was going along,
he met a man
with a load of bricks.

"Please, sir," he said,
"give me some bricks
to build me a house."

So the man gave him some bricks
and the third little pig
built himself a good, strong house.

137

One day the wolf
came knocking at his door.
"Little pig, little pig,"
he called. "Let me come in!"
But the third little pig said:
"No, no, I won't let you in—
not by the hair of my chinny-chin-chin."
"Well then," said the wolf,
"I'll huff and I'll puff
and I'll blow your house down."
So he huffed and he puffed
and he huffed and he puffed . . .
and he huffed and he puffed,
but he just <u>couldn't</u>
blow the house down!

 138

This made the wolf angry,
but he only said,
"Little pig, I know where
there's a field of turnips."

"Oh, where?" asked the third little pig.

"Right down the road,"
said the wolf. "I'll come for you
at ten o'clock tomorrow morning,
and we'll go together."

The next morning the little pig
got up at nine o'clock
and hurried to the turnip field.
He was back safe in his house
when the wolf came knocking.

"Little pig," said the wolf.
"It's time to go."

"Oh, I already got myself
a nice basket of turnips,"
the little pig said.

This made the wolf very angry,
but he just said,
"Little pig, I know where
there's a big apple tree."

"Oh, where?" asked the little pig.

"Across the meadow,"
said the wolf.
"I'll come for you tomorrow
at nine o'clock.
We'll go together."

The next morning the little pig
got up at eight o'clock.
He was busy picking apples
when he saw the wolf coming.

"Here's an apple for you!"
the little pig called,
and he threw it so far
the wolf had to chase after it.
Then the little pig
climbed down and ran away.

As soon as the little pig
was safe in his house,
the wolf came knocking.

"Little pig," he said,
"tomorrow there's going to be
a fair in town.
I'll come for you at eight o'clock."

141

The next morning the little pig
got up at seven o'clock
and hurried to the fair,
where he had a good time,
until he saw the wolf coming.
The little pig
jumped into a barrel to hide.
But the barrel fell over
and rolled down the hill,
faster and faster,
straight toward the wolf—
and it knocked him down!

The little pig was cooking
himself a big pot of soup
when the wolf came banging on his door.
"Little pig," he called,
"I didn't see you at the fair."

"Oh, but I saw you," said the little pig.
"I was riding home in the barrel
that knocked you down."

This made the wolf really angry,
much angrier than before.

"Little pig!" he roared.
"I've had enough of your tricks.
Now I'm coming to get you."
The wolf leaped
onto the little pig's roof
and he threw himself
down the little pig's chimney,
and he fell right into the pot of soup
and was cooked.

   That night, the third little pig
had wolf soup for supper.

   Yumm-yum!

Baby rabbits in nest

ANIMAL HOMES
Illa Podendorf

Many animals
make their homes
on top of the ground.

Cottontail rabbits make nests
in fields in the spring.
A cottontail's nest is warm.
It is made from soft grass and lined with fur.
The mother lines the nest
with fur from her own body.
In winter, cottontails do not live in nests.
Then they live under a barn
or under some corn stalks.

Sometimes white-footed mice make their nests
among plants on top of the ground.

Mice

A fox does not
do much building
to make its home.
It finds a hollow log
or a hole among the rocks
and makes its den there.

Fox cubs in their den

Some animal homes are above the ground.

145

Sometimes squirrels make nests
of twigs and leaves and grass in branches of trees.
Other times squirrels make homes
in holes in trees.
These homes are usually their winter homes.

Squirrel

Squirrel nest

Raccoons live near water in woods.
Some raccoons make their homes
in hollow trees.

Raccoon nest

A garden spider lives among plants.
A garden spider spins a web.
It stays on or near its web.

Spider web

Some animal homes
are under the ground.

Ground squirrels build homes
under the ground.
Their home is a long hall.
This hall is called a tunnel.
Sometimes the ground squirrels
leave a pile of dirt at the door
to their home.

Badgers live underground, too.
If you look for them, it is easy to see
where they dig their tunnels.

Skunks often make their homes
in holes in the ground.
They sometimes dig new holes.
But they may use a hole
that some other animal has made.
Sometimes skunks crawl under buildings
and make their homes there.

Ground squirrel

Badger den

Skunk nest

Some kinds of ants build their homes underground.
They dig on and on until they have
a long tunnel underground.
Ants make more than one tunnel.
At the end of each tunnel they make a room.
In an ant home there are many tunnels
and many rooms.
The first room to be made is a nursery.
The baby ants live here.
Many of the rooms are storerooms for food.
The worker ants bring back food
to put in the storerooms.

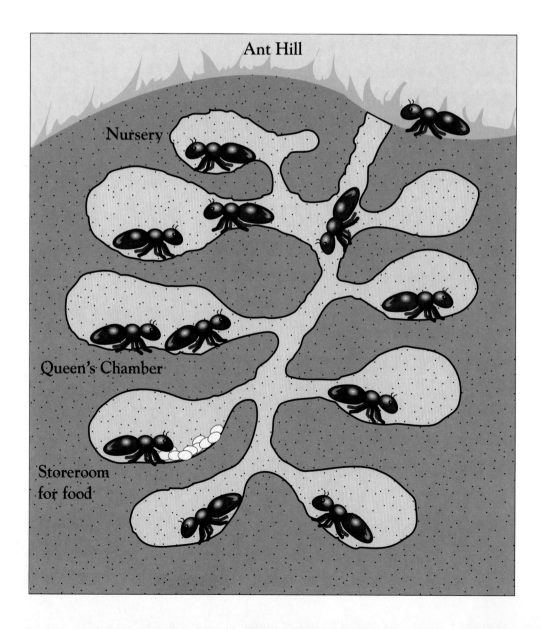

Beaver lodge

Beaver

Some animal homes are in water.

Beavers build their homes in water.
A beaver's home has a big room above water.
The door to the home is underwater.
A beaver swims underwater
and up into the room of his home.

Sunfish make a nest at the bottom of a pond.
The father brushes a place clean with his fins.
Then the mother fish lays her eggs.
They both protect the nest from their enemies.

Sunfish

Woodchuck burrow

Chickadee nest

Remember, animals live in many places.

Some animals live in the ground.
Some animals live high above the ground.
Some animals live in water.
Other animals live on land.

 150

Alligator and turtles

Elk

Deer

Some animals live in the woods.
Others live on the desert.

Some kinds of animals
build unusual homes.
Each animal home is just right
for the animal that builds
and lives in it.

Horned toad

151

Spittlebug home

Hornet nest

MAKE A HOME

Nancy Pemberton
illustrated by Barbara Bruno

You can make a home for worms.
You will need:
- a big glass jar with a wide mouth
- loose soil
- pebbles mixed with soil
- earthworms
- lettuce and cornmeal for the worms to eat
- black paper and tape

1. Fill the bottom of the jar with pebbles mixed with soil. Add loose soil to fill most of the jar. Keep the soil moist.

2. Put small pieces of lettuce and some cornmeal on top of the soil.

3. Dig up some earthworms
   and put them in the jar.

4. Tape black paper to the sides
   of the jar for one week.
   That will make the worms
   tunnel near the glass.

5. Take off the black paper.
   Watch how the worms move and eat.

6. When you are done watching the worms,
   return them to their outdoor home.

HOME FOR A BUNNY

Margaret Wise Brown

illustrated by Garth Williams

"Spring, Spring, Spring!" sang the robin.

"Spring, Spring, Spring!" sang the frog.

"Spring!" said the groundhog.

It was Spring.

The leaves burst out.

The flowers burst out.

And robins burst out of their eggs.

It was Spring.

 154

In the Spring a bunny came down the road.
He was going to find a home of his own.
A home for a bunny,
A home of his own,
Under a rock,
Under a stone,
Under a log,
Or under the ground.
Where would a bunny find a home?

"Where is your home?"
he asked the robin.
"Here, here, here," sang the robin.
"Here in this nest is my home."
"Here, here, here," sang the little robins
who were about to fall out of the nest.
"Here is our home."
"Not for me," said the bunny.
"I would fall out of a nest.
I would fall on the ground."

So he went on looking for a home.
"Where is your home?" he asked the frog.
"Wog, wog, wog," sang the frog.
"Wog, wog, wog,
Under the water,
Down in the bog."
"Not for me," said the bunny.
"Under the water, I would drown in a bog."

So he went on looking for a home.
"Where do you live?" he asked the groundhog.
"In a log," said the groundhog.
"Can I come in?" said the bunny.
"No, you can't come in my log,"
said the groundhog.

So the bunny went down the road.
Down the road and down the road he went.
He was going to find a home of his own.
A home for a bunny,
A home of his own,
Under a rock
Or a log
Or a stone.
Where would a bunny find a home?
Down the road
and down the road
and down the road
he went, until—

He met a bunny.
"Where is your home?"
he asked the bunny.

"Here," said the bunny.
"Here is my home.
Under this rock,
Under this stone,
Down under the ground,
Here is my home."

"Can I come in?"
said the bunny.
"Yes," said the bunny.
And so he did.

And that was his home.

161

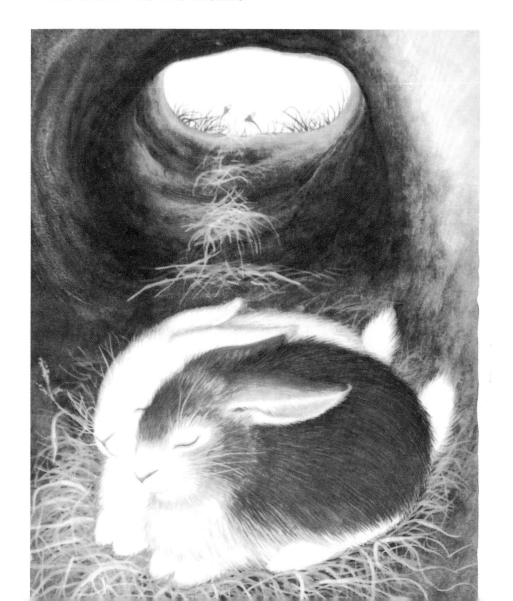

THE RABBIT WARREN

Marie Aubinais

illustrated by Monique Félix

The baby rabbits
are born in a burrow
underground.

Their mother has
prepared a nest of fur
for them. And each
morning she feeds her
babies.

Then she closes
the nest and goes out
to eat.

When the baby
rabbits are a bit older,
they move into their
parents' burrow.

Their parents live
close to other rabbit
families. All of the
burrows together are
called a warren.

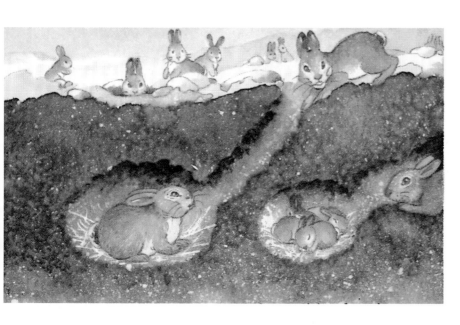

The rabbits go to the bathroom in a special place outside their burrows.

Each morning and evening the rabbits go out to eat. When it is nice and safe outside, they take a walk.

If any rabbit senses danger, it warns its family by thumping the ground very hard with its hind legs.

When a rabbit is chased, it quickly runs back to the safety of its burrow.

But when it is calm, the rabbits move around in small groups and eat grass, roots, and greens.

165

And whenever a rabbit gets its paws wet, it licks them dry.

IS THIS A HOUSE FOR HERMIT CRAB?

Megan McDonald

illustrated by S. D. Schindler

Hermit Crab was forever growing
too big for the house on his back.
It was time to find a new house.
He crawled up out of the water looking
for something to hide in, where he
would be safe from the pricklepine fish.
He stepped along the shore, by the sea,
in the sand . . . *scritch-scratch, scritch-scratch*

. . . until he came to a rock.

Is this a house for Hermit Crab?

Turning himself around, Hermit Crab backed
his hind legs beneath the rock. The rock
would not budge. It was too heavy.

So he stepped along the shore, by the sea,
in the sand . . . *scritch-scratch, scritch-scratch* . . .
until he came to a rusty old tin can.

Is this a house for Hermit Crab?

When he tried to walk with the can on his back,
it bumped and clunked. It was too noisy.

So he stepped along the shore, by the sea,
in the sand . . . *scritch-scratch, scritch-scratch*

167 🐚

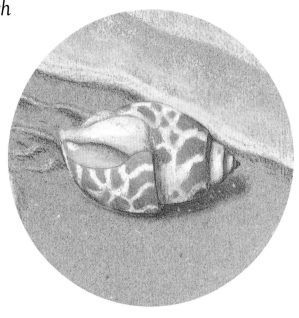

. . . until he came to a piece of driftwood.

Is this a house for Hermit Crab?

Hermit Crab crawled deep inside the rounded hollow at one end. It was too dark.

So he stepped along the shore, by the sea, in the sand . . . *scritch-scratch, scritch-scratch . . .* until he came to a small plastic pail.

Is this a house for Hermit Crab?

Climbing up toward the rim, *oops!* he fell right in. He clawed, and he clawed, until he climbed back out. It was too deep.

So he stepped along the shore, by the sea, in the sand . . . *scritch-scratch, scritch-scratch*

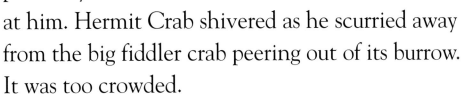

. . . until he came to a nice
round hole in the sand.

Is this a house for
Hermit Crab?

He poked his head down
into the opening. A huge
pair of eyes blinked back
at him. Hermit Crab shivered as he scurried away
from the big fiddler crab peering out of its burrow.
It was too crowded.

So he stepped along the shore, by the sea,
in the sand . . . *scritch-scratch, scritch-scratch* . . .
until he came to a fishing net.

Is this a house for Hermit Crab?

Poking his claws into the heap, he got tangled and
caught. Hermit Crab wriggled and wriggled until he
found his way out of the net. It had too many holes.

So he stepped along the shore, by the sea,
in the sand . . . *scritch-scratch, scritch-scratch*.

. . . All of a sudden a gigantic wave tossed and
tumbled pebbles and sand over Hermit Crab's head.
He swirled and whirled with the tide and
was washed back out to sea.

Sleeker than a shark, the pricklepine fish darted
out from its hiding place in the tall seaweed.
Every spine on its back stood straight as a steeple.
Mouth open wide, it headed right for Hermit Crab.

Hermit Crab raced across the ocean floor . . .
scritch-scritch-scritch-scritch

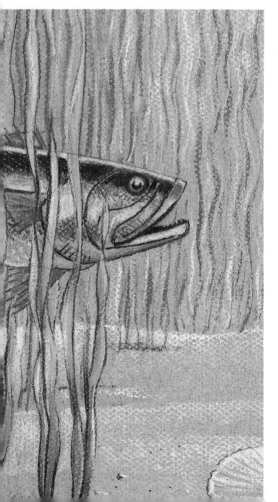

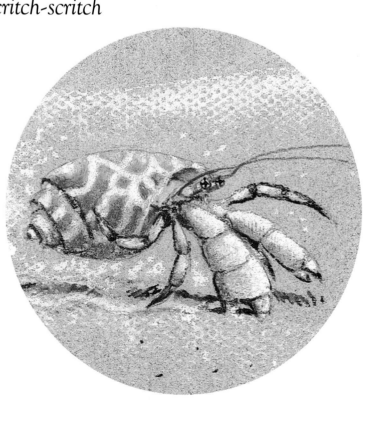

. . . scurrying behind the first creature he saw.

It was a sea snail, and he hoped it would hide him,
but the shell was empty.

The shell was empty!

Hermit Crab scrambled inside as quick as a flash,
and clamped his claw over the opening in the shell.

The pricklepine fish circled the snail shell three times, but he could not catch sight of the crab he had been chasing. He glided off in search of something else to eat.

When all seemed still and quiet, Hermit Crab snuggled comfortably down into his new shell.

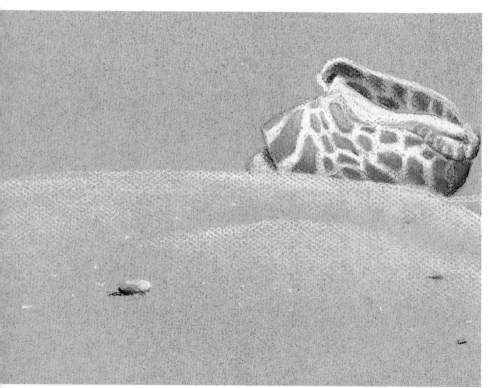

It was not too heavy, not too noisy, not too dark, and not too deep. It was not too crowded and did not have too many holes.

At last, Hermit Crab had found a new home. And it fit just right.

MEET MEGAN McDONALD, AUTHOR

Megan McDonald has worked as a storyteller and in libraries since she was fifteen years old. Is This a House for Hermit Crab? started as a story told with puppets. Children liked the story so much that she wrote it as a picture book. Now more children can read and enjoy the story.

BIBLIOGRAPHY

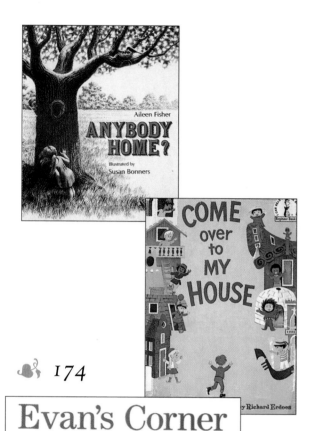

Anybody Home?
by Aileen Fisher
If you like rhymes, you will love
this book about animals and their homes.

Come over to My House
by Theo. Le Seig
A boy looks at different kinds of houses
from around the world.

Evan's Corner
by Elizabeth Starr Hill
Evan finds a place of his own
in his crowded house.
How does Evan make his corner special?

A House for Hermit Crab
by Eric Carle
Hermit Crab outgrows his old shell
and moves into a new one.
Now he must make it feel like home.

A House Is a House for Me
by Mary Ann Hoberman
Have fun learning about different kinds
of houses with this book of rhymes.

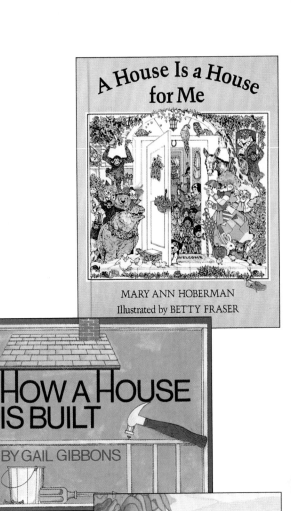

How a House Is Built
by Gail Gibbons
Read about the many kinds of workers
and tools it takes to build a house.

The Jungle Is My Home
by Laura Fischetto
People are cutting down jungle trees.
Now many animals must look
for new homes.

The Little House
by Virginia Lee Burton
A little house lives happily
in the country. Then her life changes
as a city springs up around her.

GLOSSARY

PRONUNCIATION KEY

a as in at

ā as in late

â as in care

ä as in father

e as in set

ē as in me

i as in it

ī as in kite

o as in ox

ō as in rose

ô as in bought and raw

oi as in coin

o͝o as in book

o͞o as in too

or as in form

ou as in out

u as in up

ûr as in turn; germ, learn, firm, work

ə as in about, chicken, pencil, cannon, circus

ch as in chair

hw as in which

ng as in ring

sh as in shop

th as in thin

th as in there

zh as in treasure

The mark (ˊ) is placed after a syllable with a heavy accent, as in **chicken** (chikˊ ən).

The mark (ˊ) after a syllable shows a lighter accent, as in **disappear** (disˊ ə pērˊ).

absolutely (ab′ sə lo͞ot′ lē) <u>adv.</u>
Without any doubt; for certain.

admired (ad mīrd′) <u>adj.</u> Well
thought of.

average (av′ ər ij) <u>adj.</u> Ordinary;
like most others.

batter (bat′ ər) <u>n.</u> Flour, milk,
eggs, and sugar mixed together
to make a cake.

boa constrictor (bō′ ə
kən strik′ tər) <u>n.</u> A snake that
kills its prey by squeezing.

bog (bog) <u>n.</u> A swamp; a marsh.

bog

breathe (brḛ̄th) <u>v.</u> To take air in
and blow air out.

bricklayer (brik′ lā′ ər) <u>n.</u> A
person who builds walls
out of bricks or
concrete blocks.

budge (buj) <u>v.</u> To move
a little bit.

builder (bil′ dər) <u>n.</u> A person
who builds or makes things,
such as houses.

bulldozer (bo͝ol′ dō′ zər) <u>n.</u> A
large machine that a person
rides like a tractor while
the machine pushes stones, dirt,
and trees out of the way.

burrow (bûr′ ō) <u>n.</u> A hole or
tunnel under the ground
that an animal digs to live in.

177

Pronunciation Key: at; lāte; câre; fäther; set; mē; it; kīte; ox; rōse; ô in bought; coin; bŏŏk; tōō; form; out; up; tûrn; ə sound in about, chicken, pencil, cannon, circus; chair; **hw** in **wh**ich; ri**ng**; **sh**op; **th**in; **th**ere; **zh** in treasure.

burst (bûrst) <u>n.</u> A small, quick explosion.

burst (bûrst) <u>v.</u> To come out suddenly and strongly.

🐦 _178_

calm (käm) <u>adj.</u> Still; quiet; peaceful.

carpenter (kär´ pən tər) <u>n.</u> A person who makes things out of wood.

cement (si ment´) <u>n.</u> A mixture of sand, water, and crushed stone that dries as hard as stone.

chamber (chām´ bər) <u>n.</u> A special room.

clamp (klamp) <u>v.</u> To hold tightly.

claw (klô) <u>n.</u> 1. A sharp, curved nail on an animal's foot. 2. The hard, pincher part at the end of a crab's or lobster's legs.

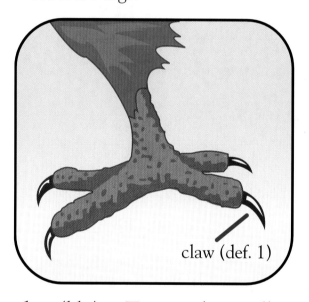

claw (def. 1)

claw (klô) <u>v.</u> To scratch or pull up by using hands, nails, or claws.

clench (klench) <u>v.</u> To close tightly.

clever (klev´ər) <u>adj.</u> Smart.

cliff (klif) <u>n.</u> The high, steep side of rock or earth.

cliff

clumsy (klum´ zē) <u>adj.</u> Likely to trip or bump into things.

clunk (klungk) <u>v.</u> To hit hard; to make a loud noise.

couch (kouch) <u>n.</u> A wide, soft chair; a sofa.

cozy (kō´ zē) <u>adj.</u> Snug; comfortable.

crash (krash) <u>v.</u> To fall and hit the ground hard.

curd (kûrd) <u>n.</u> Soft cheese; the lumps in cottage cheese.

den (den) <u>n.</u> A wild animal's home.

den

179

desert (dez´ ərt) <u>n.</u> A large area of very dry land.

driftwood (drift´ wŏŏd´) <u>n.</u> A piece of wood floating in the water or washed up onto a beach.

droop (drōōp) <u>v.</u> To bend or curve down.

Pronunciation Key: at; lāte; câre; fäther; set; mē; it; kīte; ox; rōse; ô in bought; coin; boŏk; tōō; form; out; up; tûrn; ə sound in about, chicken, pencil, cannon, circus; chair; hw in which; ring; shop; thin; there; zh in treasure.

drown (droun) <u>v.</u> To die from being kept under water and not able to breathe air.

eager (ē´ gər) <u>adj.</u> Excited about doing something.

electrician (i lek trish´ ən) <u>n.</u> A person who puts electrical wires in a building.

enemy (en´ ə mē) <u>n.</u> Someone who wants to hurt another.

engineer (en´ jə nēr´) <u>n.</u> The person who drives a train.

Eskimo (es´ kə mō´) <u>n.</u> One name for people who live in cold, Arctic regions.

exclaim (ik sklām´) <u>v.</u> To say something suddenly and loudly.

fiddler crab (fid´ lər krab´) <u>n.</u> A small, round shellfish with one claw larger than the others.

flop (flop) <u>v.</u> To fall suddenly.

forest (for´ ist) <u>n.</u> A large area of trees.

forest

frighten (frīt´ n) <u>v.</u> To scare;
to make someone afraid.

frightened (frīt´ nd) <u>adj.</u> Afraid;
scared.

gather (gath´ ər) <u>v.</u> To collect;
to bring together.

generally (jen´ ər ə lē) <u>adv.</u>
Most of the time.

gigantic (jī gan´ tik) <u>adj.</u> Very big;
huge.

goblin (gob´ lin) <u>n.</u> A very tiny,
make-believe person who often
gets into trouble.

grain (grān) <u>n.</u> The seed
of a plant like wheat.

ground (ground) <u>n.</u> The earth;
dirt.

ground (ground) <u>v.</u> Crushed
into a powder.

hare (hâr) <u>n.</u> A gray or brown
animal that looks like a large
rabbit.

hare

hind (hīnd) <u>adj.</u> At the back.

181

hind

hoe (hō) <u>v.</u> To dig in the soil
with a garden tool.

Pronunciation Key: at; lāte; câre; fäther; set; mē; it; kīte; ox; rōse; ô in bought; coin; bŏŏk; tōō; form; out; up; tûrn; ə sound in about, chicken, pencil, cannon, circus; chair; hw in which; ring; shop; thin; then; zh in treasure.

hollow (hol′ ō) adj. Empty inside.

hollow (hol′ ō) n. A hole; an empty space.

houseboat (hous′ bōt′) n. A flat-bottomed boat that is set up like a house that people can live in.

joke (jōk) n. Something that won't ever work.

joy (joi) n. A feeling of happiness.

junk (jungk) n. Something that is not worth anything; trash.

laugh (laf) v. To make a sound that shows something is funny.

laughter (laf′ tər) n. The sound a person makes when something is funny.

lightning (līt′ ning) n. A flash of electricity across the sky.

lodge (loj) n. The home of an animal or group of animals, especially beavers.

lodge

meadow (med´ ō) n. An open field covered with grass and wildflowers.

mend (mend) v. To sew up holes; to fix by sewing.

mill (mil) n. A place where workers grind grain into flour.

moist (moist) adj. A little wet; damp.

neighbor (nā´ bər) n. A person who lives near another.

nonsense (non´ sens) n. Foolishness; silliness.

nursery (nûr´ sə rē) n. A room set apart for young animals or babies.

pace (pās) n. The speed of walking or running.

pair (pâr) n. Two things that are alike or almost alike.

palm (päm) n. A tall tree with leaves that look like big fans or feathers.

pebble (peb´ əl) n. A small stone.

Pronunciation Key: at; lāte; câre; fäther; set; mē; it; kīte; ox; rōse; ô in bought; coin; bŏŏk; tōō; form; out; up; tûrn; ə sound in about, chicken, pencil, cannon, circus; **ch**air; **hw** in **wh**ich; ri**ng**; **sh**op; **th**in; **th**ere; **zh** in treasure.

peek (pēk) <u>v.</u> To look quickly.

peer (pēr) <u>v.</u> To look at something as if studying it.

perhaps (pər haps´) <u>adv.</u> Maybe.

picture (pik´ chər) <u>n.</u> A perfect example.

pleasant (plez´ ənt) <u>adj.</u> Nice.

plod (plod) <u>v.</u> To walk slowly and heavily.

plumber (plum´ ər) <u>n.</u> A person who puts water pipes into a building.

porch (porch) <u>n.</u> A covered entrance on the front or back of a house, like a room with a roof but no walls.

praise (prāz) <u>v.</u> To say nice things about someone.

prepare (pri pâr´) <u>v.</u> To make ready; to plan.

protect (prə tekt´) <u>v.</u> To keep safe.

pueblo (pweb´ lō) <u>n.</u> A group of houses built on top of each other, made of stone or adobe bricks.

pueblo

quite (kwīt) <u>adv.</u> Very.

quiver (kwiv´ ər) <u>v.</u> To shake; to tremble; to shiver.

rain forest (rān´ for´ ist) <u>n.</u> A hot area with a lot of rain where many trees grow tall and close together.

rain forest

reed (rēd) <u>n.</u> A tall grass plant with a hollow stem.

refuse (ri fyōōz´) <u>v.</u> To say no to something.

reply (ri plī´) <u>v.</u> To answer; to say.

ripe (rīp) <u>adj.</u> Fully grown; ready for eating.

scamper (skam´ pər) <u>v.</u> To run lightly or playfully.

scramble (skram´ bəl) <u>v.</u> To crawl quickly.

scurry (skûr´ ē) <u>v.</u> To run quickly.

sense (sens) <u>v.</u> To come to know.

shall (shal) <u>v.</u> Will.

shiver (shiv´ ər) <u>v.</u> To shake because of fear.

shout (shout) <u>v.</u> To call loudly.

sleeker (slēk´ ər) <u>adj.</u> More smooth.

smack (smak) <u>v.</u> To hit.

snooze (snōōz) <u>v.</u> To sleep for a short time; to doze; to take a nap.

185

Pronunciation Key: at; lāte; câre; fäther; set; mē; it; kīte; ox; rōse; ô in bought; coin; bŏŏk; tōō; form; out; up; tûrn; ə sound in about, chicken, pencil, cannon, circus; chair; hw in which; ring; shop; thin; ᵺere; zh in treasure.

snort (snort) <u>v.</u> To blow air noisily through the nose.

somersault (sum´ ər sôlt´) <u>n.</u> A turn that is made by rolling head over heels.

somersault

spine (spīn) <u>n.</u> A hard, sharp point that sticks out of the top of a fish.

spine

squeal (skwēl) <u>v.</u> To make a loud, high cry.

stalk (stôk) <u>n.</u> The stem of a plant.

steam (stēm) <u>n.</u> A mist that rises from boiling water.

steeple (stē´ pəl) <u>n.</u> A tall, pointed top on a tower or church.

stilt (stilt) <u>n.</u> A pole or a long stick that is used to hold something up.

stilt

stomach (stum´ ək) <u>n.</u> The middle part of a person's body.

straw (strô) <u>n.</u> The dried stems of plants.

stroll (strōl) <u>v.</u> To walk slowly.

stumble (stum´ bəl) <u>v.</u> To walk in a clumsy way.

suggest (səg jest´) <u>v.</u> To tell an idea; to give a plan.

supposed to (sə pōzd´ to͞o) <u>v.</u> Expected to.

swirl (swûrl) <u>v.</u> To spin around quickly.

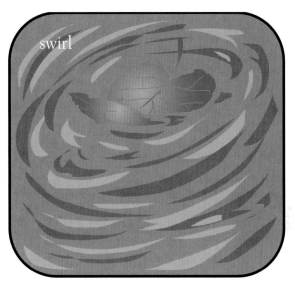

swirl

tend (tend) <u>v.</u> To take care of; to watch over.

thirsty (thûr´ stē) <u>adj.</u> Needing something to drink.

thud (thud) <u>n.</u> A sound made when something falls.

thump (thump) <u>v.</u> To beat.

Pronunciation Key: at; lāte; câre; fäther; set; mē; it; kīte; ox; rōse; ô in bought; coin; bŏŏk; tōō; form; out; up; tûrn; ə sound in about, chicken, pencil, cannon, circus; chair; hw in which; ring; shop; thin; there; zh in treasure.

thunder (thun´ dər) n. A loud noise heard after lightning.

thunderstorm (thun´ dər storm´) n. A storm with thunder and lightning.

tide (tīd) n. The rise and fall of the sea.

tide

tin (tin) n. A shiny, silver metal.

tired (tīrd) adj. Sleepy.

tongue (tung) n. The part inside the mouth that helps a person talk.

tortoise (tor´ təs) n. A large land turtle.

tortoise

tough (tuf) adj. Strong.

trailer (trā´ lər) n. A small house on wheels.

tremble (trem´ bəl) v. To shake; to shiver.

188

tuffet (tuf´ it) <u>n</u>. A low seat.

turnip (tûr´ nip) <u>n</u>. A vegetable with a large, round root that is eaten.

turnip

typical (tip´ i kəl) <u>adj</u>. Usual; the regular kind.

ugly (ug´ lē) <u>adj</u>. Not pleasant looking.

unusual (un yōō´ zhōō əl) <u>adj</u>. Strange; rare; different from most others.

usually (yōō´ zhōō əl ē) <u>adv</u>. Most of the time.

vacuum (vak´ yōōm) <u>v</u>. To clean with a machine that picks up dirt.

vine (vīn) <u>n</u>. A plant that has a very long stem. A vine can grow along the ground or up a wall.

vine

189 ❦

warren (wor´ ən) <u>n</u>. A place where many rabbits live.

Pronunciation Key: at; lāte; câre; fäther; set; mē; it; kīte; ox; rōse; ô in bought; coin; bŏŏk; tōō; form; out; up; tûrn; ə sound in about, chicken, pencil, cannon, circus; **ch**air; **hw** in **wh**ich; ri**ng**; **sh**op; **th**in; **th**ere; **zh** in treasure.

wheat (hwēt) <u>n.</u> A plant that has seeds that can be eaten or made into flour.

wheat

whey (hwā) <u>n.</u> The part of milk that becomes like water when milk is being made into cheese.

whirl (hwûrl) <u>v.</u> To spin around quickly.

whirl

wriggle (rig′ əl) <u>v.</u> To twist; to squirm.

yank (yangk) <u>v.</u> To pull quickly and hard.

COLOPHON

*This book has been designed in the
classic style to emphasize our commitment
to classic literature. The typeface,
Goudy Old Style, was drawn in 1915 by
Frederic W. Goudy, who based it on
fifteenth-century Italian letterforms.*

*The art has been drawn to reflect the
golden age of children's book illustration
and its recent rebirth in the work of
innovative artists of today. This book was
designed by John Grandits. Composition,
electronic page makeup, and photo and
art management were provided by
The Chestnut House Group, Inc.*